"The first thing that attracted me to Luann was the way Greg drew her lying across the bed with her head hanging down as she talked to Bernice. It's easy to forget that cartooning is the drawing of funny pictures, and Luann's position is certainly a funny picture. Like all of us, she seems to be surrounded by people who have a better idea as to what is going on. Luann feels she has nothing going for her. She doesn't like her looks and she is always at least two days behind in school. Her counselor doesn't even come close to being able to reach her problems, much less solve them. If you add up some of these things, you get a life which is pretty depressing, but fortunately for the reader, Luann is fun to be around. Obviously, she would be surprised at this because at her age there doesn't seem to be much hope. I like to think that years from now she will look back upon this period of her life and be able to laugh, but I also seriously doubt it. If there were only some way that all of us could realize that being thirteen years old is not the worst thing in the world. I wish we could tell Luann to relax and enjoy herself, because basically, she is a neat kid and we all like her."

—CHARLES M. SCHULZ

Meet Luann

by GREG EVANS

A Byron Preiss Visual Publications, Inc. Book

Pacer BOOKS FOR YOUNG ADULTS

BERKLEY BOOKS, NEW YORK

To Betty, for all the years...

The comic strips in this book have
been previously published in syndication.

MEET LUANN

A Berkley/Pacer Book, published by arrangement with
Byron Preiss Visual Publications, Inc.

PRINTING HISTORY
Berkley/Pacer edition / June 1986

ISBN: 0-425-08878-2

JUST ONCE,
I'D LIKE TO
GET A GRADE
THAT I COULDN'T
POSSIBLY GET

IF AARON HILL INVITES ME TO THE DANCE, I'LL *DIE!* IF HE DOESN'T ASK ME, I'LL DIE. IF HE ASKS TIFFANY, I'LL DIE. IF GUNTHER ASKS ME, I'LL DIE. IF NO ONE ASKS ME, I'LL DIE

CAN I HAVE YOUR SKATES AND YOUR STEREO?

greg
3·23

© News America Syndicate. 1985.

HOW DO YOU KNOW IF YOU'RE LOSING WEIGHT?

© News America Syndicate, 1985

4·5

17

DEAR DIARY: 11 AM, SATURDAY. I WAITED ALL WEEK FOR <u>THIS</u>?

Luann

Luann

WHAT'CHA DOIN', LUANN?

OH.. I'M JUST TRYING TO FIGURE OUT WHAT I CAN DO TO MAKE MY ROOM LOOK MORE ATTRACTIVE AND FEMININE

4-13

LEAVE

greg

Luann

Luann

Luann

I DON'T THINK COUNSELING IS HELPING ME, MISS PHELPS. I'M MORE MIXED UP NOW THAN WHEN I FIRST BEGAN THESE SESSIONS!

© News America Syndicate 1985

COUNSELOR

4·30

WHEN WAS THAT, ANYWAY?

COUNSELOR

THE DAY BEFORE YESTERDAY

COUNSELOR

5·2

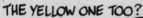

Luann

© News America Syndicate, 1985

Luann

GUNTHER FOLLOWED ME AROUND ALL DAY!

HE'S THE MOST HOMELY, CREEPY, NERDY GUY IN THE WHOLE SCHOOL! WHY'S HE PICK *ME* TO HANG AROUND?

gREg
5·6

HE PROBABLY FEELS SORRY FOR YOU

46

Luann

BRAD, DID YOU HAVE A HAPPY CHILDHOOD?

YEAH, I DID. RIGHT UP 'TIL 13 YEARS AGO

WHY, WHAT HAPP—

5-11

greg

DEAR DIARY: I WORRY
ABOUT MY FIRST KISS...
I JUST *KNOW* I'LL TILT
MY HEAD THE WRONG WAY...

52

WHEN I WAS IN SECOND GRADE, I THOUGHT I KNEW EVERYTHING. NOW I'M IN SEVENTH GRADE AND I FEEL LIKE I KNOW NOTHING

COUNSELOR

BY THE TIME I'M IN THE TWELFTH GRADE, I'LL BE A COMPLETE IDIOT

COUNSELOR

GREG
5-20

Luann

greg
5·23

Luann

BRAD! LOOK AT THE MESS YOU MADE! PEANUT BUTTER SMEARED ON THE COUNTER, CRUMBS ALL OVER, JELLY DRIPPED ON THE FLOOR—

I JUST *CLEANED* THIS KITCHEN!

GREG 5-24

WHAT FOR?

Luann

© News America Syndicate, 1985

greg
5-25

© News America Syndicate, 1985

greg 5-27

Luann

© News America Syndicate, 1985

greg
5-28

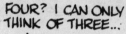

Luann

THE SECRET OF PUTTING ON HAIRSPRAY IS TO NOT PUT ON TOO MUCH

© News America Syndicate, 1985.

PERFECT!

greg
6·1

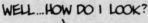

Luann

DON'T LOOK AT ME, BRAD

I'M TRYING NOT TO...

BUT YOU KNOW HOW YOU CAN'T HELP STARING AT A GORY ACCIDENT?

Luann

TONIGHT I HAVE TO CALL BERNICE, DO MY FINGERNAILS, CATCH UP ON MY DIARY, WATCH "MAGNUM P.I." AND READ MY TEEN MAGAZINE

NOW *HOW* AM I SUPPOSED TO FIND TIME TO DO HOMEWORK?

6-12

75

WELL, HERE'S THE END OF ANOTHER SCHOOL YEAR. HOW MANY OF YOU FEEL YOU REALLY LEARNED SOMETHING IN MY CLASS?

© News America Syndicate, 1985

PUT YOUR HAND DOWN, LUANN

GREG

6-14

HOW DEPRESSING.
FOR $7.98 I CAN
BUY A CALCULATOR
THAT'S SMARTER
THAN I AM

SPECIAL SALE!

greg

6·15

© News America Syndicate, 1985

© News America Syndicate, 1985

81

Luann

I JUST SPENT TWO HOURS MOWING, RAKING AND TRIMMING THE LAWN AND YOU WANT TO *SIT* ON IT ?!!

DEAR DIARY: WELL, BERNICE AND
I ARE HERE IN MY ROOM...SITTIN'
ROUND...NOT DOIN' ANYTHING...
...JUST SITTIN'.....

WANNA
ADD
ANYTHING?

NO, I THINK
YOU PRETTY
MUCH
COVERED IT

GREG
6-26

ANOTHER FUN-FILLED MOMENT
CAPTURED FOREVER

CLICK

Luann

DEAR DIARY: THIRTEEN'S A CRUMMY AGE...
TOO OLD FOR TOYS...TOO YOUNG FOR BOYS...

© News America Syndicate, 1985

BEING A TWEENAGER IS THE PITS

greg
6-27

"TO BE 'IN' THIS SUMMER, YOUR WARDROBE SHOULD HAVE THAT CAREFREE AND CASUAL LOOK"

Luann

A POEM: "TO AGE THIRTEEN" by Luann

SOMETIMES I FEEL WONDERFUL
SOMETIMES I'M DEPRESSED
OFTEN I AM CAREFREE
OFTEN I FEEL STRESS
AT TIMES I'M INDEPENDENT
AT TIMES I'M SO DEPENDING...
I WONDER IF, AT AGE 13,
LIFE'S STARTING OR JUST ENDING?

DEAR DIARY: IT'S JULY 17th,
9:15 P.M. ONLY FOUR YEARS,
ONE MONTH, 20 DAYS, TWO
HOURS AND 45 MINUTES
'TIL I'M 18!

106

MOM? DAD? BRAD? ARE YOU ALL READY TO SEE ME IN MY NEW SWIMSUIT?

WE'RE READY, LUANN

ZOOM

WELL?...

GREG 7-24

Luann

DAD? LUANN'S MOM SAID I COULD HAVE DINNER HERE IF IT'S OK WITH YOU.

GREAT! THANKS, DAD! 'BYE!

MOM, BERNICE'S DAD SAID SHE COULD HAVE DINNER HERE IF IT'S OK WITH YOU...

GREG
8.2

Luann

GULP
MULCH

WHY ARE BOYS SO TOTALLY GROSS!!?

GLUG GLUG

© News America Syndicate. 1985

8-3

WHICH BOYS ARE YOU REFERRING TO?

greg

Luann

"I was born in Los Angeles in 1947 and grew up in Burbank, California.

"While other boys my age were playing Roy Rogers, I was drawing cartoons. My dream was to work for Walt Disney or *MAD* Magazine.

"But they never called. So I went off to college at California State University in Northridge where I majored in art, minored in English and graduated in 1970 with a Bachelor of Arts degree and a teaching credential.

"I taught junior and senior high school art for four years before realizing that I hated teaching.

"I got married, had a couple of kids (which I still have, by the way: Gary 10 and Karen 7) and moved to Colorado Springs to live in the clean air and snow. I wound up working at a TV station as promotion manager and graphic artist.

"But by 1980, we were tired of snow, so we moved back to Southern California and settled in our current home in San Marcos. I began a new career: I bought a robot and hired out to entertain at trade shows, fairs and promotions.

"In February, 1984, I submitted "Luann" to News America Syndicate; just one more effort in a fifteen-year attempt to get syndicated. I promised my wife that this would be my final try. Fortunately, NAS signed me in November and "Luann" landed in driveways on March 17, 1985 ... lucky St. Patrick's Day."

—GREG EVANS